ROALD DAHL

SPOTTY POWDER
AND OTHER SPLENDIFEROUS SECRETS

Illustrated by Quentin Blake

PUFFIN

Find out more about Roald Dahl by visiting the website at **roalddahl.com**

PUFFIN BOOKS

UK | USA | Canada | Ireland | Australia
India | New Zealand | South Africa

Puffin Books is part of the Penguin Random House group of companies
whose addresses can be found at global.penguinrandomhouse.com.

www.penguin.co.uk
www.puffin.co.uk
www.ladybird.co.uk

Penguin
Random House
UK

Extracts taken from: *The Roald Dahl Diary 1992* first published 1991; *Charlie's Secret Chocolate Box*
first published 1997; *D is for Dahl* first published 2004; *The Dahlmanac* first published 2006;
Dahlmanac 2 first published 2007; *More About Boy* first published 2008 – all published in
Puffin Books; *Roald Dahl's Cookbook* published by Penguin Books 1996.
'Spotty Powder' first published in *Puffin Post* Vol.7, No.1, 1973; 'Strawberry-flavoured Chocolate-
coated Fudge' from *Roald Dahl's Revolting Recipes* published by Jonathan Cape Ltd 1994.
First published 2010
This abridged edition first published 2016
001

Text design by Dan Newman. Set in Adobe Caslon Pro and Filosofia
Printed in Great Britain by Clays Ltd, St Ives plc

A CIP catalogue record for this book is available from the British Library

ISBN: 978–0–141–37799–5

All correspondence to
Puffin Books
Penguin Random House Children's
80 Strand, London WC2R ORL

www.greenpenguin.co.uk

How Roald Dahl started writing Charlie and the Chocolate Factory

'*Charlie and the Chocolate Factory* took me a terrible long time to write. The first time I did it, I got everything wrong. I wrote a story about a little boy who was going round a chocolate factory and he accidentally fell into a big tub of melted chocolate and got sucked into the machine that made chocolate figures and he couldn't get out. It was a splendid big chocolate figure, a chocolate boy the same size as him. And it was Easter time, and the figure was put in a shop window, and in the end a lady came in and bought it as an Easter present for her little girl, and carried it home. On Easter Day, the little girl opened the box with her present in it, and took it out and then she decided to eat some of it. She would start with the head, she thought. So she broke off the nose, and when she saw a real human nose sticking out underneath and two big bright human eyes staring at her through the eye-holes in the chocolate, she got a nasty shock. And so it went on.

'But the story wasn't good enough. I rewrote it, and rewrote it, and

Mike Teavee

the little tentacles kept shooting out from
my head, searching for new ideas, and at
last one of them came back
with Mr Willy Wonka and his
marvellous chocolate factory
and then came Charlie and
his parents and grandparents
and the Golden Tickets and
the nasty children, Violet
Beauregarde and Veruca Salt and
all the rest of them.

'As a matter of fact, I got so
wrapped up in all those nasty
children, and they made me giggle so much
that I couldn't stop inventing them. In the
first full version of *Charlie and the Chocolate
Factory*, I had no less than ten horrid little

Violet
Beauregarde

boys and girls. That was too many. It became confusing. It wasn't a good book. But I liked them all so much, I didn't want to take any of them out.

'One of them, who was taken out in the end, was a horrid little girl who was disgustingly rude to her parents and also thoroughly disobedient. Her name was Miranda Mary Piker . . .'

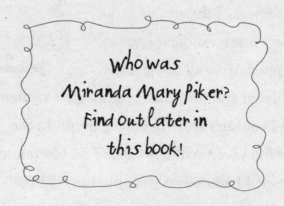

Who was
Miranda Mary Piker?
Find out later in
this book!

Roald Dahl's Year

Nature is full of secrets if you look hard enough. And Roald Dahl kept notes about the habits of butterflies and frogs, the colour and songs of birds, and the different flowers, plants and berries that blossomed in the countryside. Find out what Roald Dahl liked or disliked about every month of the year, including his favourite animals and birds. (And read about some of the hilarious pranks he got up to when he was a young boy too!)

RoALD DahL's January

'For the last twelve months we have all been living in one year and now all of a sudden it is another. It is extraordinary how this tremendous change takes place in the space of a fraction of a second. As the clock approaches midnight on the thirty-first of December you are still in the old year, but then all at once, one millionth of a second after midnight, you are in the new. I have always found this sudden change from one year to another awfully hard to get used to, and all through the new January that follows I keep writing down the old year instead of the new one on letters and other bits of paper . . .

'There is just one small bright spark shining through the gloom in my January garden. The first snowdrops are in flower.'

The Missing Children

As you now know, Roald Dahl wrote several versions of *Charlie and the Chocolate Factory* and included lots of very naughty characters. In a very early draft of the story, as many as *ten* children are lucky Golden Ticket finders who each win a tour of Mr Wonka's Chocolate Factory:

Augustus Pottle who falls in the chocolate river
Miranda Grope who also falls in after him

Wilbur Rice and Tommy Troutbeck who climb in wagons running from the vanilla fudge mountain and end up in the Pounding and Cutting Room

Violet Strabismus who turns purple after chewing the three-course-meal gum

Clarence Crump, Bertie Upside and Terence Roper who each cram a whole mouthful of warming candies and end up overheating

Elvira Entwhistle who falls foul of the squirrels in the Nut Room

And Charlie Bucket who gets stuck inside a chocolate statue and witnesses a burglary – and receives a very unusual reward . . .

Roald Dahl soon decided there were too many naughty children in the story. So, somewhat reluctantly, he reduced the number of lucky Golden Ticket finders to seven, and gave all the children distinct characteristics:

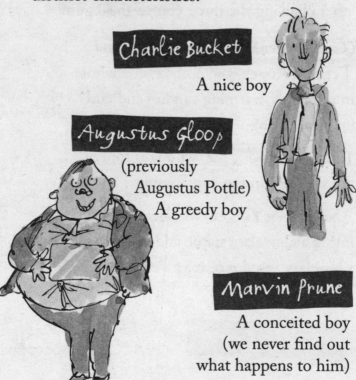

Charlie Bucket

A nice boy

Augustus Gloop

(previously
Augustus Pottle)
A greedy boy

Marvin Prune

A conceited boy
(we never find out
what happens to him)

Herpes Trout

A television-crazy boy
(he became Mike Teavee
in the final version!)

Veruca Salt

A girl who
is allowed
to HAVE
anything she
wants

A girl who
chews gum all
day long

Violet Beauregarde

And one more . . .

Miranda Mary Piker

A girl who is allowed to DO anything she wants

And it is in this draft that Charlie's grandparents are introduced for the first time, and tiny people called 'Whipple-Scrumpets' become Mr Wonka's workforce, reciting poems as each child leaves.

Roald Dahl's February

'Only once have I discovered a new molehill in our orchard in the month of February. I love seeing molehills because they tell me that only a few inches below the surface some charming and harmless little fellow is living his own private busy life scurrying up and down his tunnels hunting for food . . .

    'Do you know anything about moles? They are remarkable animals. They are shy and gentle and their fur coats are softer than

velvet. They are so shy that you will seldom
see one on the surface . . . The molehills that

you see are not of course their houses.
They are simply piles of loose soil that a mole
has pushed up out of the way because, after all,
if you are digging an underground tunnel you
have to put the excavated soil somewhere.

'His food consists of worms, leather-
jackets, centipedes and beetle grubs, and
the fantastic thing is that he actually has to
eat *one half of his own body weight* of these
tiny delicacies every single day in order to
stay alive! No wonder he's a busy fellow.
Just imagine how much food *you* would have
to eat to consume half your own body weight!
Fifty hamburgers, one hundred loaves of
bread and a bucketful of Mars Bars *and* the
rest of it each and every day. It makes one
quite ill to think about it! '

The Whipple-Scrumpets

Have a look at an early version of the Whipple-Scrumpets' song about greedy Augustus Gloop, and compare it to the one that actually appears in *Charlie and the Chocolate Factory*, sung by the Oompa-Loompas. Can you spot the differences?

The Whipple-Scrumpets . . .
began dancing about and clapping
their hands and singing:
Augustus Gloop! Augustus Gloop!
The great big greedy nincompoop!

How long could we allow this beast
To gorge and guzzle, feed and feast
On everything he wanted to?
Great Scott! It simply wouldn't do!
And so, you see, the time was ripe
To send him shooting up the pipe;
He had to go. It had to be.
And very soon he's going to see
Inside the room to which he's gone
Some funny things are going on.

But don't, dear children, be alarmed.
Augustus Gloop will not be harmed,
Although, of course, we must admit
He will be altered quite a bit.
For instance, all those lumps of fat
Will disappear just like that!
He'll shrink and shrink and shrink and shrink,
His skin will be no longer pink,
He'll be so smooth and square and small
He will not know himself at all.
Farewell, Augustus Gloop, farewell!
For soon you'll be a caramel!'

'They're teasing,' Mr Wonka said,
shaking a finger at the singing
Whipple-Scrumpets. 'You mustn't
believe a word they say.'

Mr Wonka's Chocolate Factory Recipe

Strawberry-flavoured Chocolate-coated Fudge

You will need:

20 x 25 cm shallow baking tin

Greaseproof paper

Large saucepan

Sugar thermometer

Cutters

450 g caster sugar

100 g unsalted butter

175 ml evaporated milk

A few generous drops of pink food-colouring

A generous ½ tsp (2.5 ml) of strawberry food-flavouring

100 g melted chocolate for dipping

Makes enough for ten greedy children

How to make:

1. Line the tin with buttered greaseproof paper.

2. Put all the ingredients except the flavouring and colouring into a large heavy-bottomed saucepan and place over a low heat.

3. Stir occasionally. Once the sugar has dissolved, gently boil the mixture and now stir all the time (to prevent sticking and burning on the bottom of the pan).

4. Place the sugar thermometer into the saucepan and boil the mixture to a soft ball (118°C). This takes about five minutes.

5 Take the pan off the heat, stir until the bubbles subside and then add the flavouring and the colouring.

6 Beat rapidly with a wooden spoon until the mixture thickens and becomes granular, approximately three minutes.

7 Pour the fudge into the lined tin and leave to set. If necessary, smooth with a palette knife dipped into boiling water.

8 With shaped cutters, cut out the fudge and dip one side into the melted chocolate, or decorate with piped chocolate, creating different patterns.

Please ask a grown-up to help you when you are handling anything hot.

Roald Dahl's
March

'I rather like the month of March . . . your heart is lifted by the signs of approaching spring all around you. Halfway through the month most of the hedges are covered with a pale powdering of green as the little leaf buds begin to burst, and the pussy willows are smothered in yellow pollen. Crocuses are flowering brilliantly and best of all, the nesting season is beginning to get seriously under way . . . I can see a pair of blackbirds

building high up in the trunk of the big
clipped yew tree . . . I watch a thrush carrying
bits of dry grass up into the branches of the
vine . . . I see a pair of blue tits popping in and
out of a small hole in the wooden tool shed . . .
I see a pair of robins making a mossy nest in
the bank underneath the heather bed . . .

'By the end of the month ladybirds are on the wing once again, and you will notice that nearly all of them are the two-spotted kind. Peacock butterflies and small tortoiseshells are emerging from their winter sleep, hunting for early flowers. Bumblebees and honeybees have also woken up and are in among the crocuses, looking for pollen.'

Meet Quentin Blake

Roald Dahl and Quentin Blake make a perfect partnership of words and illustrations, but when Roald started writing, he had many different illustrators. Quentin started working with him in 1976 (the first book he illustrated was *The Enormous Crocodile*, published in 1978) and from then on they worked together until Roald's death. Quentin ended up illustrating all of Roald Dahl's books, with the exception of *The Minpins*.

To begin with, Quentin was a bit nervous about working with such a very famous author, but by the time they collaborated on *The BFG*, they had become firm friends. Quentin never knew anything about a new story until the manuscript arrived. 'You'll have some fun with this,' Roald would say – or, 'You'll have some trouble with this.' Quentin would make lots of rough drawings to take along to Gipsy House, where he would show them to Roald and see what he thought. Roald Dahl liked his books to be packed with illustrations – Quentin ended up drawing twice as many pictures for *The BFG* as he had originally been asked for.

Quentin Blake was born on 16 December 1932. His first drawing was published when he was sixteen, and he has written and illustrated many of his own books, as well as Roald Dahl's. Besides being an illustrator he taught for over twenty years at the Royal College of Art – he is a real professor!

What Roald Dahl thought of Quentin Blake

'It is Quent's pictures rather than my own
written descriptions that have brought
to life such characters as the BFG, Miss
Trunchbull, Mr Twit and The Grand High
Witch. It is the faces and the bodies
he draws that are remembered by
children all over the world . . .
When he and I work together on
a new book and he has a pen in
his hand, it is magical to watch
the facility with which he can
sketch out a character or a scene.

"You mean more like this?" he will say, and the nib will fly over the paper at incredible speed, making thin lines in black ink, and in thirty seconds he has produced a new picture. "Perhaps," I will say, "he should have a more threatening look about him." Once again the pen flies over the paper and there before you is exactly what you are after. But this is not to say that I "help" him with many of the characters he draws for my books. Most of them he does entirely on his own and they are far better and funnier than anything I could think of.'

Ideas Books

Roald Dahl kept two ideas books for about forty years. They were both old school exercise books, the first of which was sandy coloured, and the second red and very battered. He thought that good ideas were like dreams – soon forgotten – and made sure that he wrote them down straight away. He then ticked the really good ideas and crossed out the ones he had used. Some ideas were developed years and years after they were jotted down. Can you guess

A story about the fox who has a whole network of underground tunnels leading to all the shops in the village. At night, he goes up through the floorboards and helps himself.

What about a chocolate factory that makes fantastic and marvellous things — with a crazy man running it?

which books came from these ideas?
If Roald Dahl hadn't been an author, he
could have been a doctor, a boxer, a golfer,
an inventor, a scientist, a botanist or a picture
framer. He had a natural talent for all of

these things. And he was interested in just about EVERYTHING. But here are a few of the things he was especially fascinated by:

Nineteenth- and twentieth-century paintings
Eighteenth-century English furniture
Gardening
Orchids
Music
Wine
Gambling
Good food
Chocolate

Roald Dahl once said, 'If I were a headmaster I would get rid of the history teacher and get a chocolate teacher instead.'

Roald Dahl's April

'Now at last we can say that spring has arrived, and with it come flocks of summer migrants, all those little birds that flew away to the warmer countries in the south when it began to get cold last October. Most of them go as far as North Africa and don't ask me how they find their way there and back again because that is one of the great mysteries of the world. There are skylarks, greenfinches, goldfinches, whitethroats, willow-warblers,

golden plovers, blackcaps, swallows, house-
martins, chiffchaffs and many more besides,
and soon after they arrive they pair up and
start to build their nests.'

Roald Dahl's
May

'May is the month of the cuckoo . . .
Everyone living in the countryside knows
when the cuckoos start arriving because you
cannot help hearing the loud, eerie, almost
human call of the male bird. It quite literally
says, "Cuck-koo, cuck-koo," and the voice
carries for miles . . . Unlike most other birds,
cuckoos do not pair up and stay together,
so there are no marriages or family life in
cuckooland. No cuckoo has ever bothered to

build its own nest or hatch or feed its young.
The female (carrying her egg in her beak)
searches the hedgerows until she finds the
nest of another bird that already has eggs
in it, and she slips her own egg in with the

others and flies away and forgets all about it.

'. . . The mother hedge sparrow doesn't
seem to mind at all and proceeds to sit on
the egg and incubate it together with her
own. Little does she know what is going
to happen when all the eggs hatch . . . the
cuckoo chick grows three times as fast as the
little sparrows. The overgrown baby cuckoo
proceeds quite literally to push the baby
hedge sparrows one by one out of the nest
to die, and in the end all that is left is this
grotesque, huge, fluffy cuckoo chick filling
the entire nest. The hedge sparrow parents
don't seem to notice what has happened
and they go on feeding this murderer until
in the end it is big enough to hop out of
the nest and fly away without so much
as a thank you!'

Roald's Family Holidays

SPRING

Roald Dahl's father died when Roald was only three so his mother brought up him and his sisters on her own.

Every Easter she rented a house in Tenby, Wales, and took all the children there for a holiday.

The house, called The Cabin, was right
next to the sea. When the tide was in,
the waves broke right up against one wall
of the house. Roald and his sisters used
to collect winkles and eat them on slices
of bread and butter.

Roald Dahl's
June

'June is the month of the foxglove,
perhaps the most beautiful of all the wild
flowers. The foxglove also gives us a drug
called digitalis which is valuable to doctors
in treating heart conditions. Barley is already
standing tall in the fields. Don't confuse it
with the other two main cereals, wheat and
oats. Barley has long itchy spikes covering the
seeds, and if you pick one of these heads and
slip it under the sleeve of your jacket or shirt

with the long spikes pointing downwards, the head will actually climb all the way up to your shoulder as you walk along swinging your arm.

'During this month the tadpoles in the ponds are beginning to sprout tiny arms and legs, and soon they will be turning into small frogs. Be nice to frogs, by the way. They are your friends in the garden. They eat the beastly slugs and never harm your flowers.

There is so much beauty in the countryside
in June. The lovely pink dog roses are
in full bloom along the hedges and wild
honeysuckle is plentiful.

'I'm afraid that if you live in a town you
don't see any of these splendid sights . . .'

A Missing Chapter

The following secret chapter was originally included in *Charlie and the Chocolate Factory*. But because there were too many naughty children in the earlier versions of the book, 'Spotty Powder' – and the revolting Miranda Mary Piker – had to be dropped.

Luckily, Roald Dahl kept it in a very safe place, so you could read it here ...

Spotty Powder

'This stuff,' said Mr Wonka, 'is going to cause chaos in schools all over the world when I get it in the shops.'

The room they now entered had rows and rows of pipes coming straight up out of the floor. The pipes were bent over at the top and they looked like large walking sticks. Out of every pipe there trickled a stream of white crystals. Hundreds of Oompa-Loompas were running to and fro, catching

44

the crystals in little golden boxes and stacking the boxes against the walls.

'Spotty Powder!' exclaimed Mr Wonka, beaming at the company. 'There it is!' That's it! Fantastic stuff!'

'It looks like sugar,' said Miranda Piker.

'It's meant to look like sugar,' Mr Wonka said. 'And it tastes like sugar. But it isn't sugar. Oh, dear me, no.'

'Then what is it?' asked Miranda Piker, speaking rather rudely.

'That door over there,' said Mr Wonka, turning away from Miranda and pointing to a small red door at the far end of the room, 'leads directly down to the machine that makes the powder. Twice a day, I go down there myself to feed it. But I'm the only one. Nobody ever comes with me.'

They all stared at the little door on which it said MOST SECRET – KEEP OUT.

The hum and throb of powerful machinery could be heard coming up from the depths below, and the floor itself was vibrating all the time. The children could feel it through the soles of their shoes.

Miranda Piker now pushed forward and stood in front of Mr Wonka. She was a nasty-looking girl with a smug face and a smirk on her mouth, and whenever she spoke it was always with a voice that seemed to be saying, 'Everybody is a fool except me.'

'OK,' Miranda Piker said, smirking at Mr Wonka. 'So what's the big news? What's this stuff meant to do when you eat it?'

'Ah-ha,' said Mr Wonka, his eyes sparkling with glee. 'You'd never guess that, not in a million years. Now listen. All you have to do is sprinkle it over your cereal at breakfast-time, pretending it's sugar. Then you eat it. And then, exactly five seconds after that, you come out in bright red spots all over your face and neck.'

'What sort of a silly ass wants spots on his face at breakfast-time?' said Miranda Piker.

'Let me finish,' said Mr Wonka. 'So then your mother looks at you across the table and says, "My poor child. You must have chickenpox. You can't possibly go to school today." So you stay at home. But by lunch-time, the spots have all disappeared.'

'Terrific!' shouted Charlie. 'That's just what I want for the day we have exams!'

'That is the ideal time to use it,' said Mr Wonka. 'But you mustn't do it too often or it'll give the game away. Keep it for the really nasty days.'

'Father!' cried Miranda Piker. 'Did you hear what this stuff does? It's shocking! It mustn't be allowed!'

Mr Piker, Miranda's father, stepped forward and faced Mr Wonka. He had a smooth white face like a boiled onion.

'Now see here, Wonka,' he said. 'I happen to be the headmaster of a large school, and I won't allow you to sell this rubbish to the children! It's . . . criminal! Why, you'll ruin the school system of the entire country!'

'I hope so,' said Mr Wonka.

'It's got to be stopped!' shouted Mr Piker, waving his cane.

'Who's going to stop it?' asked Mr Wonka. 'In my factory, I make things to please children. I don't care about grown-ups.'

'I am top of my form,' Miranda Piker said, smirking at Mr Wonka. 'And I've never missed a day's school in my life.'

'Then it's time you did,' Mr Wonka said.

'How dare you!' said Mr Piker.

'All holidays and vacations should be stopped!' cried Miranda. 'Children are meant to work, not play.'

'Quite right, my girl,' cried Mr Piker, patting Miranda on the top of the head. 'All work and no play has made you what you are today.'

'Isn't she wonderful?' said Mrs Piker, beaming at her daughter.

'Come on then, Father!' cried Miranda. 'Let's go down into the cellar and smash the machine that makes this dreadful stuff!'

'Forward!' shouted Mr Piker, brandishing his cane and making a dash for the little red door on which it said MOST SECRET – KEEP OUT.

'Stop!' said Mr Wonka. 'Don't go in there! It's terribly secret!'

'Let's see you stop us, you old goat!' shouted Miranda.

'We'll smash it to smithereens!' yelled Mr Piker. And a few seconds later the two of them had disappeared through the door.

There was a moment's silence.

Then, far off in the distance, from

somewhere deep underground, there came
a fearful scream.

'That's my husband!' cried Mrs Piker,
going blue in the face.

There was another scream.

'And that's Miranda!' yelled Mrs Piker,
beginning to hop around in circles.
'What's happening to them? What have
you got down there, you dreadful beast?'

'Oh nothing much,' Mr Wonka answered.
'Just a lot of cogs and wheels and chains
and things like that, all going round and
round and round.'

'You villain!' she screamed. 'I know your
tricks! You're grinding them into powder!
In two minutes my darling Miranda will
come pouring out of one of those dreadful
pipes, and so will my husband!'

'Of course,' said Mr Wonka. 'That's part of the recipe.'

'It's what!'

'We've got to use one or two schoolmasters occasionally or it wouldn't work.'

'Did you hear him?' shrieked Mrs Piker, turning to the others. 'He admits it! He's nothing but a cold-blooded murderer!'

Mr Wonka smiled and patted Mrs Piker gently on the arm.

'Dear lady,' he said, 'I was only joking.'

'Then why did they scream?' snapped Mrs Piker. 'I distinctly heard them scream!'

'Those weren't screams,' Mr Wonka said. 'They were laughs.'

'My husband never laughs,' said Mrs Piker.

Mr Wonka flicked his fingers, and up came an Oompa-Loompa.

'Kindly escort Mrs Piker to the boiler room,' Mr Wonka said. 'Don't fret, dear lady,' he went on, shaking Mrs Piker warmly by the hand. 'They'll all come out in the wash. There's nothing to worry about. Off you go. Thank you for coming!

Farewell! Goodbye! A pleasure to meet you!'

'Listen, Charlie!' said Grandpa Joe. 'The Oompa-Loompas are starting to sing again!'

'Oh, Miranda Mary Piker!' sang the five Oompa-Loompas, dancing about and laughing and beating madly on their tiny drums.

'Oh, Miranda Mary Piker,
How could anybody like her,
Such a priggish and revolting little kid.
So we said, "Why don't we fix her
In the Spotty-Powder mixer
Then we're bound to like her better than
    we did."

Soon this child who is so vicious
Will have gotten quite delicious,
And her classmates will have surely
    understood
That instead of saying, "Miranda!
Oh, the beast! We cannot stand her!"
They'll be saying, "Oh, how useful
And how good!"'

Roald Dahl's
July

'Sunday afternoons were the only times
we had free throughout the school week,
and most boys went for long walks in the
countryside. But I took no long Sunday
afternoon walks during my last term.
My walks took me only as far as the garage in
Wilmington where my lovely motorbike was
hidden. There I would put on my disguise –
my waders and helmet and goggles and wind
jacket – and go sailing in a state of absolute
bliss through the highways and byways of
Derbyshire. But the greatest thrill of all was

to ride at least once every Sunday afternoon
slap through the middle of Repton village,
sailing past the pompous prefects and the

masters in their gowns and mortarboards.
. . . Don't forget that those were the days
when schools like mine were merciless
places where serious misdemeanours were
punished by savage beatings that drew blood
from your backside. I am quite sure that if I
had ever been caught, that same headmaster
would have thrashed me within an inch of
my life and would probably have expelled
me into the bargain. That is what made it
so exciting. I never told anyone, not even
my best friend, where I went on my Sunday
walks. I had learnt from a tender age that
there are no secrets unless you keep them
to yourself and this was the greatest secret
I had ever had to keep in my life so far. '

Weird and wonderful Roald Dahl facts

He was very tall – six feet five and three-quarter inches, or nearly two metres. His nickname in the RAF was Lofty, while Walt Disney called him Stalky (because he was like a beanstalk!).

————— ✳ —————

He was a terrible speller, but he liked playing **Scrabble**.

His nickname at home was the Apple, because he was the apple of his mother's eye (which means her favourite!).

He pretended to have appendicitis when he was nine because he was so homesick in his first two weeks at boarding school. He fooled the matron and the school doctor and was sent home. But he couldn't fool his own doctor, who made him promise never to do it again.

He didn't like **cats** – but he did like dogs, birds and goats.

Roald Dahl wrote the screenplay for the James Bond film *You Only Live Twice*.

He once had a tame magpie.

──── ✳ ────

He was a keen photographer at school and, when he was eighteen, won two prizes: one from the Royal Photographic Society in London and another from the Photographic Society of Holland.

──── ✳ ────

In the churchyard at Great Missenden, Buckinghamshire, big friendly giant footprints lead to Roald Dahl's grave.

Roald Dahl's August

'I find August in England a rather torpid month. The trees and plants have all done their growing for the year and nature is hanging motionless in suspension before sinking slowly into the decline of winter. There is a brownish look to the countryside and the leaves are hanging heavy on the trees. But if it is nothing else, it is the month of the butterfly. Butterflies are lovely things. They do no harm to man himself either by

stinging, biting or spreading disease.
Nor are they beneficial to man as the
silkworm is or the honeybee. The large
white or cabbage butterfly is the only one
that is a nuisance because it lays eggs on
your cabbages and these hatch out into
horrid hungry caterpillars . . .

'August is, by the way, the month
when young adders are born in heathy,
hilly places, and baby grass snakes emerge
from their eggs in rotting leaves and old
compost heaps. It is the month when
hedgehogs have their litters of babies,
all born blind and helpless, and I'm afraid
it is also the month when wasps come
on the warpath, stinging humans in
great numbers.'

Advice from Roald Dahl

'At the age of eight I became a mad diary enthusiast . . . I was a bit of a loner in those days and a bit of a dreamer and some of the things I wrote down for the next five or six years were thoughts that I don't think I would have dared even to speak out aloud to myself. That's the beauty of writing. You find that you can actually write things down that are quite outlandish and outrageous and you feel all the better for it.'

'I have a passion for teaching kids to become readers, to become comfortable with a book, not daunted. Books shouldn't be daunting, they should be funny, exciting and wonderful; and learning to be a reader gives a terrific advantage.'

Roald Dahl's September

'I have always loved this month. As a schoolboy I loved it because it is the Month of the Conker . . . We all know, of course, that a great conker is one that has been sorted in a dry place for at least a year. This matures it and makes it rock hard and therefore very formidable. We also know about the short cuts that less dedicated players take to harden their conkers. Some soak them in vinegar for a week.

Others bake them in the oven at a low temperature for six hours. But such methods are not for the true conker player. No world-champion conker has ever been produced by short cuts . . .

'The best conker I ever had was a conker 109, and I can still remember that frosty morning in the school playground when my one-o-nine was finally shattered by Perkins's conker 74 in an epic contest that lasted over half an hour. After it, I felt even more shattered than my conker!'

Roald Dahl's October

'This, like September, is a lovely month, mild and misty and smelling of ripe apples. We have a small orchard at the back of our house . . . there was so much fruit every autumn that I told all the children in the village they could come in at any time and ask to borrow a ladder and pick what they wanted. They came in droves . . .

'During October swarms of migrant birds cross the North Sea from Scandinavia to our

shores. Some, like starlings and blackbirds
and thrushes and rooks and jackdaws,
will stay here for the winter. Others, like the
skylarks and goldcrests and finches, will rest
before going on south to spend the winter
in Africa . . .

'At this time of year our hedges are covered with old man's beard and woody nightshade. Hips and haws make splashes of crimson everywhere. In the grassy banks on either side, an enormous number of different wild flowers and ferns grow. On weekends I see groups of enthusiastic botanists from London hunting for rare specimens. They walk slowly up the lane peering into the banks and calling to one another when they find something interesting. I like these people. I like enthusiasts of any kind.'

Roald Dahl's November

'November is the middle of what we used
to call the Christmas term. I had my first
Christmas term away from home when I was
eight years old. And it is also the month of
fireworks and Guy Fawkes. Oh, how we used
to look forward to the fifth of November at
boarding school . . . We had jackie jumpers,
Roman candles, crack-bangers, fire-
serpents, big bombers, rockets and
golden rain!

'There is a badger's earth in the wood above our house, and this month the badgers are busy digging their deep winter quarters and lining them with dry leaves for warmth. Before November is out, they will have blocked up the entrances to their holes and will sleep the winter through. Like the badgers, the grass snakes are all starting to hibernate, but they are not as domesticated as the badgers. They have no real homes and simply hide themselves among the twisted tree roots underneath the hedges, and quite often they will coil themselves around each other for comfort. For many small animals, the approach of winter means the time to go to sleep until spring arrives again. It would make life a lot more comfortable if we could do the same!'

Roald Dahl's Secret Writing Tips

'The job of a children's writer is to try to write a book that is so exciting and fast and wonderful that the child falls in love with it.'

Have you got what it takes to be an author? You might well have – it's just that you don't know it yet!

Believe it or not, Roald Dahl only found out he could write by accident. At the age of twenty-six he was 'discovered' by C. S. Forester, author of the Captain Horatio Hornblower stories. From that moment, he never stopped writing.

But it's not easy. These are the qualities Roald Dahl suggested you will need if you are going to become a writer:

1   'You should have a lively imagination.
2   You should be able to write well. By that I mean you should be able to make a scene come alive in the reader's mind.

3   You must have
stamina. In other
words, you must be
able to stick to what
you are doing and
never give up.

4   You must be a
perfectionist. That means you must
never be satisfied with what you have
written until you have rewritten it again
and again, making it as good as you
possibly can.

5   You must have strong self-discipline.

6   It helps a lot if you have a keen sense
of humour.

7   You must have a degree of humility.
The writer who thinks that his work
is marvellous is heading for trouble.'

Point 4 is crucial.
Roald Dahl spent
many months writing
Charlie and the Chocolate
Factory and, as you know, there was a first
draft, then a second, then a third, and so
on. Some bits were added in, other bits
taken out. With each rewrite, the story
would get better and better.

Roald Dahl's
December

'One Christmas, when I was about nine or ten, I had been given a fine Meccano set as my main present, and I decided I would make a device that was capable of 'bombing' from the air the pedestrians using the public footpath across our land.

'Briefly my plan was as follows: I would stretch a wire all the way from the high roof of our house to the old garage on the other side of the footpath. Then I would construct from my Meccano a machine that would hang from the wire by a grooved wheel and this machine would hopefully run down the wire at great speed dropping its bombs on the unwary walkers underneath.

'Next morning, filled with the enthusiasm that grips all great inventors, I climbed on to the roof of our house by the skylight and wrapped one end of the long roll of wire around a chimney. I threw the rest of the wire into the garden below and went back down myself through the skylight. I carried the wire across the garden, over the fence, across the footpath, over the next fence and into our land on the other side. I now pulled the wire very tight and fixed it with a big nail to the top of the door of the old garage. So far so good.

'Next I set about constructing from the
Meccano my bombing machine, or chariot
as I called it. I put the wheel at the top, and
then running down from the wheel I made a
strong column about two feet long (a metre).
At the lower end of this column, I fixed two
arms that projected outwards at right angles,
one on either side, and along these arms
I suspended five empty Heinz soup tins.
The whole thing looked something like this:

'. . . I filled all the soup tins with water.
I lay flat on the roof waiting for a victim.
Soon two ladies dressed in tweed skirts
and jackets and each wearing a hat, came
strolling up the path with a revolting little
Pekinese dog on a lead. I knew I had to time
this carefully, so when they were very nearly
but not quite directly under the wire, I let
my chariot go. Down she went, making a
wonderful screeching-humming noise as
the metal wheel ran down the wire and the
string ran through my fingers at great speed.
Bombing from a height is never easy. I had
to guess when my chariot was directly over
the target, and when that moment came,
I jerked the string. The chariot stopped dead
and the tins swung upside down and all the
water tipped out. The ladies, who had halted

and looked up on hearing the rushing noise of my chariot overhead, caught the cascade of water full in their faces. It was tremendous. A bulls-eye first time. The women screamed. I lay flat on the roof so as not to be seen, peering over the edge, and I saw the women shouting and waving their arms. Then they came marching straight into our garden through the gate at the back and crossed the garden and hammered on the door. I nipped down smartly through the skylight and did a bunk.

'Later on my mother fixed me with a steely eye and told me she was confiscating my Meccano set for the rest of the holidays. But for days afterwards I experienced the pleasant warm glow that comes to all of us when we have brought off a major triumph!'

Charlie's Chocolate Shop

At one time, *Charlie and the Chocolate Factory* was going to end very differently! This was the ending in an earlier version:

The shop has been finished now, and it is the most beautiful chocolate shop in the world. It occupies a whole block in the centre of the city, and it is nine storeys high.

Inside it, there are moving staircases and
elevators to take the customers up and
down, and no less than one hundred ladies,
all dressed in spotless gold and chocolate
uniforms, are there to serve behind the

counters. They will sell you anything you want from a single little blue bird's egg with a tiny sugary bird inside it to a life-size chocolate elephant with huge curvy tusks and a chocolate elephant driver sitting on its back.

And Charlie Bucket, coming home from school in the evenings, nearly always brings along with him about twenty or thirty of his friends and tells them that they can choose anything they want – for free.

'It's my shop,' he says. 'Just help yourselves.'

And so they do.

Isn't it amazing how much a book can change before it is published?

Secrets are everywhere.
If you keep looking hard enough,
you might just find something new and
magical that has never been seen before.
Who knows? One day you may even
discover the secret of what it takes
to become as great a writer
as Roald Dahl!

HOW MANY HAVE YOU READ?

☐ ☐ ☐ ☐ ☐

☐ ☐ ☐ ☐ ☐

☐ ☐ ☐ ☐ ☐

MORE THAN 5 WHOOPSY-SPLUNKERS! You've got some reading to do!

MORE THAN 10 More tremendous things await – keep turning those pages

ALL OF THEM? Whoopee! Which was your favourite?

FANTASTIC
PHIZZ-WHIZZING
BOOKS
INSPIRED BY
ROALD DAHL'S
WORLD...

ROALD DAHL
SCRIBBLE BOOK
DOODLE WRITE & IMAGINE!

ROALD DAHL
THE BFG's
GLORIUMPTIOUS
STICKER
ACTIVITY BOOK

ROALD DAHL
WHIZZPOPPING
JOKE BOOK
OVER 500 HILARIOUS GAGS!

STORIES ARE GOOD FOR YOU.

Roald Dahl said,
*'If you have good thoughts, they will shine
out of your face like sunbeams and you
will always look lovely.'*

We believe in doing good things.
That's why ten per cent of all Roald Dahl income*
goes to our charity partners. We have supported
causes including: specialist children's nurses, grants for
families in need, and educational outreach programmes.
Thank you for helping us to sustain this vital work.

Find out more at roalddahl.com

The Roald Dahl Charitable Trust is a registered UK charity (no. 1119330).
* All author payments and royalty income net of third-party commissions.